The Giggle Box

Mother

Robot

Children

A play by Joy Cowley
Illustrations by Rodney McRae

Children:

Poor Robot.

He can't giggle.

He's lost his giggle box.

2

Mom:
Let's look for it
in the barn.

Children:
Here's a box.
Come here, Robot.

Robot:
Moo! Moo!

4

Mom:
That won't do.

Children:
It's not a giggle box.
It's a moo-moo box.

5

Mom:
Let's look by the pond.

Children:
Here's a box.

6

Robot:
Ribbett! Ribbett!
Ribbett! Ribbett!

Children:
It's a ribbett box.

7

Mom:
Let's look
in the chicken house.

Children:
Here's a box.
Come here, Robot.

8

Robot:
Cluck! Cluck!
Cluck! Cluck!

Mom:
That's not a giggle box.

Children:
No, it's a cluck-cluck box.

9

Mom:
Let's look in the grass.

Children:
Here's a box.
It looks like a giggle box.

Robot:
Maa! Maa! Maa!
Maa! Maa! Maa!

Children:
No, no, no!

Children:
Let's look in the garage.
Oh! Here's a box.

Mom:
That's not a giggle box.

Children:
Come here, Robot.

Robot:
Vrrm! Vrrm! Vrrm!

Children:
He likes it! He likes it!

13

Robot:
Vrrm! Vrrm! Vrrm!

Mom:
But that's not a giggle box.

Children:

It's better than a giggle box.

All:

Vrrm! Vrrm! Vrrm! Vrrm!